The Shakespeare Quiz Book

Helen Barton

First published 1995
Reprinted 1996
Reprinted 1997
Reprinted 2000
Reprinted 2002
© Helen Barton 1995

ISBN 0-9527257-0-3

Published by Helen Barton.
Printed by Aspect Design.

For Sam, Thomas and Eleanor

Contents

NAME THE PLAY

1. Thirteen plays have either "Prince" or "King" in their title. Name as many as you can.

2. Name the play which has a three word title, each word starting with "L".

3. Polonius and Horatio are characters in which play?

4. What is the full title of these four plays:
   a) "Othello"?
   b) "Hamlet"?
   c) "Twelfth Night"?
   d) "Pericles"?

5. Seven plays have place names in their titles. Name as many as you can.

6. Which one of these was the last History play to be written:
   a) "King Henry The Eighth"
   b) "King John"
   c) "King Richard The Third" ?

7. Is Benedick a character in:
   a) "A Midsummer Night's Dream"
   b) "Measure For Measure"
   c) "Much Ado About Nothing" ?

8. Name one of the early Comedies.

9. Bottom is a character in which play?

10. Name any play which has an Epilogue.

11. Give the titles of four Tragedies.

12. Name the two plays in which Angelo is a character.

13. Helena is in "A Midsummer Night's Dream". Which other play has a character with the same name?

14. Which is Shakespeare's last play?

15. Name four of the Comedies.

16. Which two plays have characters called Mariana?

17. "The Two Gentlemen Of Verona" ends with:
       "One feast, one house; one mutual happiness."
    True or false?

18. Which play opens with the appearance of Orlando and Adam?

19. Name a play which has a Prologue.

20. Which play opens with three witches?

21. Name the only play to open with the main character.

22. These are the opening lines from one of the Comedies:
       "Now, fair Hippolyta, our nuptial hour
       Draws on apace;"
    Is the play:
       a) "A Midsummer Night's Dream"
       b) "Antony And Cleopatra"
       c) "Twelfth Night" ?

23. How many plays have "King Henry" in the title?

24. Name the first Tragedy Shakespeare wrote.

25. Complete these titles:
    a) "Measure For . . . . "?
    b) "The Merry Wives Of . . . . "?
    c) "The Two Gentlemen Of . . . . "?

26. In which History play is Dr Butts "physician to the King"? Is it:
    a) "King Henry The Eighth"
    b) "King Richard The Second"
    c) "King John" ?

27. In which plays do these characters appear:
    a) Shylock
    b) Rosalind
    c) Oberon ?

28. Name the play in which these characters appear: Prospero, Miranda and Ferdinand.

29. Is Hortensio a suitor in:
    a) "All's Well That Ends Well"
    b) "Troilus And Cressida"
    c) "The Taming Of The Shrew" ?

30. In which play is Rumour, the Presenter? Is it:
    a) "Richard The Third"
    b) "King Henry The Fifth"
    c) "King Henry The Fourth - Part Two" ?

31. Falstaff appears in "The Merry Wives Of Windsor" and which two other plays?

DEATHS AND GORY BITS

1. Which character in "Julius Caesar" commits suicide by swallowing fire? Is it:
   a) Casca
   b) Calphurnia
   c) Portia ?

2. How do Romeo and Juliet die?

3. Who smothers who in "Othello"?

4. Which two characters in the same play poison themselves with an asp?

5. Of which character is this said:
   "Who, as 'tis thought, by self and violent hands
   Took off her life" ?

6. In which play does a character exit "pursued by a bear"? Extra points if you can name the character!

7. Answer these questions:
   a) Who kills Coriolanus?
   b) How?
   c) Who stands on his body?

8. Which play is this from:
   "The one the other poison'd for my sake,
   And after slew herself." ?
   Is it:
   a) "Antony And Cleopatra"
   b) "Troilus And Cressida"
   c) "King Lear" ?

DEATHS AND GORY BITS

9. Who mistakenly kills someone by kissing them with poisoned lips?

10. Which is the bloodiest of the plays?

11. Who is blinded in "King Lear"? Is it:
    a) Edgar
    b) Gloucester
    c) Edmund ?

12. In which plays are there these stage directions:
    a) "Enter a Messenger with two heads and a hand." ?
    b) "Enter a Gentleman with a bloody knife" ?

13. Who says:
    "O, I die, Horatio!
    The potent poison quite o'er-crows my spirit." ?

14. In "Macbeth" who comes in with whose head?

15. Who has her hands and tongue cut off?

16. Who in "Othello" dies after singing "Willow, willow, willow."?

17. Timon of Athens retires into his cave to die. True or false?

18. Who serves up dead sons to their mother in a pie?

19. Who says:

    "Hold then my sword, and turn away thy face,
    While I do run upon it." ?

    Is it:

    a) Coriolanus
    b) Brutus
    c) Troilus ?

20. Who says:

    "Why did you bring these daggers from the place?
    They must lie there. Go carry them, and smear
    The sleepy grooms with blood." ?

21. Which female character drowns?

22. How does Julius Caesar die?

23. In which play is there an executioner in the cast list?

24. Which character, in a play of the same name, has his hand cut off?

25. Who dies first, Antony or Cleopatra?

26. How does Hamlet die?

27. Who in "Julius Caesar" is killed in error by the Plebians?

28. In which play are the murderers sent to kill Clarence?

GHOSTS, GHOULS AND SPIRITS

1. Who says in which play:
   "How ill this taper burns! Ha! who comes here?
   I think it is the weakness of mine eyes
   That shapes this monstrous apparition." ?

2. Who says in which play:
   "Round about the cauldron go;
   In the poison'd entrails throw." ?

3. Who in "The Tempest" is described as a "savage and deformed slave"?

4. What is Puck's other name?

5. What is the name of the spirit in "The Tempest"?

6. Name the four fairies in "A Midsummer Night's Dream."

7. Where do these lines come from:
   "and there were drawn
   Upon a heap a hundred ghastly women,
   Transformed with their fear, who swore they saw
   Men, all in fire, walk up and down the streets." ?
   Is it:
   a) "Julius Caesar"
   b) "Macbeth"
   c) "Timon Of Athens" ?

8. Which ghost says to Richard the Third:
   "Let me sit heavy on thy soul to-morrow!
   Think how thou stabb'dst me in my prime of youth
   At Tewkesbury." ?

9. The ghost of Henry the Sixth says to Richard the Third:
   "When I was mortal, my anointed body
   By thee was punched full of deadly holes."
   True or false?

10. In "Julius Caesar" the ghost of Caesar appears to Brutus and tells him he will see him again. Where?

11. Where do you find this stage direction:
    "A dark cave. In the middle, a cauldron boiling."?

12. In "A Midsummer Night's Dream" who says:
    "I'll put a girdle round about the earth
    In forty minutes." ?
    Is it:
    a) Oberon
    b) Puck
    c) Titania ?

13. In which play does the first fairy say:
    "You spotted snakes with double tongue,
    Thorny hedgehogs, be not seen;" ?

14. "Hamlet" has a ghost show of eight kings. True or false?

15. In which play is there this stage direction:
    "He draws, and is charmed from moving." ?
    Is it:
    a) "The Tempest"
    b) "As You Like It"
    c) "The Comedy Of Errors" ?

16. Which goddess appears to Pericles in a vision?

17. Who says and in which play:
    "By the pricking of my thumbs,
    Something wicked this way comes." ?

18. Who says this in "A Midsummer Night's Dream":
    "If we shadows have offended,
    Think but this and all is mended,
    That you have but slumb'red here
    While these visions did appear." ?

19. The following is from "The Tempest":
    "Go make thyself like a nymph o' th' sea; be
        subject
    To no sight but thine and mine, invisible
    To every eyeball else."
    Who is speaking to whom?

20. In "Macbeth" how are the witches described in the
    list of characters?

21. Prospero says this in "The Tempest":
    "Be not afeard. The isle is full of noises,
    Sounds, and sweet airs, that give delight, and hurt
        not."
    True or false?

22. Who has magical flower juice squeezed on her eyes to
    make her fall in love with the first thing she sees?

23. In which play do these spirits appear: Iris, Juno and
    Ceres?

24. In which History play do you find in the cast list "a conjurer" and "A Spirit raised by him"? Is it:
    a) "King John"
    b) "King Henry The Sixth - Part Two"
    c) "King Henry The Fifth"

25. Which ghost says:
    "I am thy father's spirit,
    Doom'd for a certain term to walk the night,
    And for the day confin'd to fast in fires,
    Till the foul crimes done in my days of nature
    Are burnt and purg'd away." ?

FEMALE CHARACTERS

1. Who is Caesar's wife?

2. Which female character in "The Merchant of Venice" dresses up as "a Doctor of Laws"?

3. Who in "As You Like It" dresses up as a man?

4. What is the name of the fairy queen in "A Midsummer Night's Dream" ?

5. There are four characters titled "Mistress" in "The Merry Wives of Windsor". How many can you name?

6. Name the two female characters, both of whose names begin with 'C', who have plays named after them.

7. Who is the mother of Coriolanus? Is it:
   a) Volumnia
   b) Virgilia ?

8. Isabella is a character in which of these plays:
   a) "Twelfth Night"
   b) "Measure For Measure"
   c) "The Tempest" ?

9. In which play do you find a character called Silvia? Is it:
   a) "The Two Gentlemen Of Verona"
   b) "Much Ado About Nothing"
   c) "All's Well that Ends Well" ?

10. Whose mother is Gertrude?

FEMALE CHARACTERS

11. Whose widow is Lady Anne in "King Richard The Third"?

12. In "The Taming Of The Shrew", what is the name of Katherina's sister?

13. Miranda and Perdita are characters in which two plays?

14. King Lear has three daughters. What are their names?

15. Who is the main female character in "Measure For Measure"?

16. Viola has a brother called Claudio in "Twelfth Night". True or false?

17. How is Olivia described in the list of characters in "Twelfth Night"?

18. Hero is a character in "Much Ado About Nothing". Whose daughter is she?

19. Doll Tearsheet is a character in which History play?

20. About whom is this said:
     "'Twas told me you were rough, and coy, and sullen,
     "And now I find report a very liar;" ?
   Is it:
     a) Ophelia
     b) Cordelia
     c) Katherina ?

21. Who gives caskets to her suitors?

22. Portia in "Julius Caesar" wounds herself in the thigh to prove her ability to keep a secret. True or false?

23. Of whom is this said:
> "Come Lammas Eve at night shall she be fourteen." ?

24. Of whom is this said:
> "Since his Majesty went into the field, I have seen her rise from her bed, throw her nightgown upon her, unlock her closet, take forth paper, fold it, write upon't, read it, afterwards seal it, and again return to bed; yet all this while in a most fast sleep." ?

25. Which two characters say this and in which play?:
> X: "Where hast thou been, sister?"
> Y: "Killing swine"

26. Of whom is this said:
> "false, false, false!
> Let all untruths stand by thy stained name,
> And they'll seem glorious." ?

Is it:
   a) Cressida
   b) Olivia
   c) Regan ?

27. Who says:
> "I see a woman may be made a fool
> If she had not a spirit to resist." ?

28. Who says to her father:
> "Unhappy that I am, I cannot heave
> My heart into my mouth." ?

29. Who is described as "a fiend-like queen"?

30. Who says this:
    "I had rather lose the battle than that sister
    Should loosen him and me." ?

31. Who says this at the end of which play:
    "It is not the fashion to see the lady the epilogue;
    but it is no more unhandsome than to see the
    lord the prologue." ?

32. Lady Anne in "Richard the Third" delivers this curse.
    True or false?
    "If heaven have any grievous plague in store
    Exceeding those that I can wish upon thee,
    O, let them keep it till thy sins be ripe,
    And then hurl down their indignation
    On thee, the troubler of the poor world's peace!"

33. Who enters, dressed in boy's clothes and says:
    "I see a man's life is a tedious one." ?
    Is it:
    a) Rosalind
    b) Perdita
    c) Imogen ?

34. Which character says, speaking of her sister:
    "I know your lady does not love her husband;
    I am sure of that; and at her late being here
    She gave strange oeillades and most speaking
        looks
    To noble Edmund." ?

WHO SAID WHAT

1. "Friends, Romans, countrymen,"

2. "I have done the state some service, and they know't."
   Is it:
   a) Othello
   b) Hamlet
   c) Coriolanus ?

3. "A horse, a horse! my kingdom for a horse!"

4. "Then must you speak
   Of one that lov'd not wisely, but too well;"

5. Cressida says the following:
   "I have a kind of self resides with you."
   True or false?

6. "Howl, howl, howl, howl! O, you are men of stones!"

7. "Why may not that be the skull of a lawyer?"

8. "O mother, mother!
   What have you done?"
   Is it:
   a) Macbeth
   b) Coriolanus
   c) Hamlet ?

9. "The Merchant of Venice" opens with this line spoken
   by Antonio:
   "In sooth, I know not why I am so sad."
   True or false?

10. "If music be the food of love, play on,"

11. In "The Merchant of Venice" who says:
    "If you prick us, do we not bleed? If you tickle us, do we not laugh? If you poison us, do we not die?" ?

12. "Here's a knocking indeed! If a man were porter of hell-gate, he should have old turning the key."

13. Julius Caesar says:
    "But I am constant as the northern star"
    True or false?

14. In "Julius Caesar" who says this:
    "There is a tide in the affairs of men
    Which, taken at the flood, leads on to fortune;
    Omitted, all the voyage of their life
    Is bound in shallows and in miseries," ?

15. Which character says:
    "What's in a name? That which we call a rose
    By any other name would smell as sweet;" ?

16. "A bloody deed! - almost as bad, good mother,
    As kill a king and marry with his brother."

17. "The words expressly are 'a pound of flesh'."

18. "I know a bank where the wild thyme blows,"
    Is it:
    a) Titania
    b) Puck
    c) Oberon ?

19. Which character in "The Tempest" says:
    "But this rough magic
    I here abjure;" ?

20. "Thy lips rot off!"

21. "Against the Capitol I met a lion,"

22. "Neither a borrow nor a lender be;"

23. In "Othello" who says:
    "Reputation is an idle and most false imposition;
    oft got without merit, and lost without deserving."
    Is it:
    a) Othello
    b) Desdemona
    c) Iago ?

24. "But screw your courage to the sticking place,
    And we'll not fail."

25. "Alas, poor Yorick!"

SET THE SCENE

1. Where is "Romeo And Juliet" set?

2. Which play is set in Navarre? Is it:
    a) "Love's Labour's Lost"
    b) "The Comedy of Errors" ?

3. Which play is set in "Athens and a wood near it"?

4. Padua and Petruchio's house is the setting for which play? Is it:
    a) "As You Like It"
    b) "The Taming Of The Shrew" ?

5. Where is "Titus Andronicus" set?

6. "The Two Gentlemen Of Verona" is set in which other city?

7. "Twelfth Night" is set in "A city in Illyria". True or false?

8. Which two plays are set in Venice?

9. Which play is set "Dispersedly in various countries."? Is it:
    a) "Pericles"
    b) "The Winter's Tale"
    c) "Cymbeline" ?

10. What is the setting for "Macbeth"?

11. Which play's setting is described as:
    "A ship at sea; afterwards an uninhabited island"?

12. Name two plays which are set in Rome.

13. "Cymbeline" is set in Sicilia and Bohemia. True or false?

14. The scene is: "Rousillon; Paris; Florence; Marseilles". What is the play?

15. Which play is set in Vienna?

16. Which play is set in "Oliver's house; Frederick's court; and the Forest of Arden"?

17. Which play's scene is described as "The Roman Empire"?

18. Which two plays are set in Athens?

JOKERS, JESTERS AND CLOWNS

1. In which play is Trinculo the jester?

2. What role do the clowns play in "Hamlet"?

3. In which play is the clown the son of a shepherd? Is it:
   a) "The Winter's Tale"
   b) "Pericles"
   c) "The Comedy Of Errors" ?

4. There are five "irregular Humourists" in "King Henry Fourth - Part Two". Can you name any of them?

5. Match these plays to their characters:
   a) "The Tempest"
   b) "The Two Gentlemen Of Verona"
   c) "As You Like It"
   i) Speed and Launce, clownish servants
   ii) Touchstone, the court jester
   iii) Stephano, a drunken butler

6. In "Twelfth Night" which character says:
   "Well, grant it then,
   And tell me, in the modesty of honour,
   Why you have given me such clear lights of favour,
   Bade me come smiling and cross-garter'd to you,
   To put on yellow stockings, and to frown
   Upon Sir Toby and the lighter people." ?

7. In which play does Sir Andrew Aguecheek appear?

8. Launcelot Gobbo is a character in which play?

9. Launce says this in "The Two Gentleman of Verona":
   "I am but a fool, look you, and yet I have the wit to think my master is a kind of knave;"
   True or false?

10. Who says this in which play?:
    "O nuncle, court holy water in a dry house is better than this rain-water out o'door. Good nuncle, in; ask thy daughters' blessing. Here's a night pities neither wise men nor fools."

11. In which play is Froth, "a foolish gentleman"? Is it:
    a) "Measure for Measure"
    b) "Much Ado About Nothing"
    c) "The Merry Wives of Windsor" ?

12. In "As You Like It" the Duke Senior says:
    "He uses his folly like a stalking-horse, and under the presentation of that he shoots his wit."
    Of whom is he talking?

13. Which clown closes which play with this song?:
    "When that I was and a little tiny boy,
    With hey, ho, the wind and the rain,
    A foolish thing was but a toy,
    For the rain it raineth every day."

14. Which play includes Elbow "a simple constable."? Is it:
    a) "The Tempest"
    b) "Twelfth Night"
    c) "Measure For Measure" ?

FINISH THE SPEECH

(Points for every line you complete.
Number of lines given in each answer in brackets.)

1. "To be, or not to be - that is the question;" (13)

2. "The quality of mercy is not strain'd;" (4)

3. "Now is the winter of our discontent" (8)

4. "All the world's a stage," (5)

5. "But this rough magic" (8)

6. "Is this a dagger which I see before me," (7)

7. "Out, damned spot!" (7)

8. "But, soft! What light through yonder window breaks?" (5)

9. "Blow, winds, and crack your cheeks; rage, blow." (9)

10. "O Romeo, Romeo! wherefore art thou Romeo?" (4)

11. "Friends, Romans, countrymen, lend me your ears." (12)

NAME THE CHARACTER

1. Apart from the History plays, ten plays are named after the main male character. Which are they?

2. In "Romeo and Juliet" there are two Friars. One is called Friar John. Name the other.

3. There are eight conspirators in "Julius Caesar". Name at least two.

4. Name one male and one female character from these plays:
   a) "Twelfth Night"
   b) "The Taming of the Shrew"

5. Only one of the following characters appears in "Much Ado About Nothing". Is it:
   a) Benedick
   b) Malvolio
   c) Oberon ?

6. Match these characters to their plays:
   a) Rosalind   i)   "Othello"
   b) the Nurse   ii) "As You Like It"
   c) Desdemona   iii) "Romeo And Juliet"

7. Thersites is described as the "deformed and scurrilous Greek" in "Troilus and Cressida". True or false?

8. In which History plays is Hotspur a character?

9. Name two female characters from "King Lear" and two from "The Merchant of Venice".

10. Which two male characters whose names both start with "C" have plays named after them?

11. Viola and Olivia are characters in "Much Ado About Nothing". True or false?

12. Give the names of three Greek commanders in "Troilus and Cressida".

13. There are six "tradesman" characters in "A Midsummer Night's Dream." Name as many as you can.

14. Can you match these three characters from "Love's Labour's Lost" to their professions?:
    a) Dull   i)   a curate
    b) Sir Nathaniel   ii) a schoolmaster
    c) Holofernes   iii) a constable

15. Both "As You Like It" and "Love's Labour's Lost" have a female character described as "a country wench". Name them.

16. Which character in "King Henry the Fourth - Part Two" says:
    "If I had a thousand sons, the first humane principle I would teach them should be to forswear thin potations, and to addict themselves to sack."?

17. Which character says he could be described as "An honourable murderer,"? Is it:
    a) Othello
    b) Hamlet
    c) Macbeth ?

18. To which tragic hero is this said:
    "Do not for ever with thy vailed lids
    Seek for thy noble father in the dust." ?

19. Which character in a History play is described as "that bottled spider" and "this poisonous bunch-back'd toad." ?

20. Who is described thus:
    "he doth bestride the narrow world
    Like a Colossus, and we petty men
    Walk under his huge legs, and peep about
    To find dishonourable graves." ?

21. In the same play, the villain and the tragic hero each kill their wives. What are the characters' names?

22. Julius Caesar says this about Brutus:
    "He thinks too much. Such men are dangerous."
    True or false?

23. Who speaks these lines and about whom?:
    "She wakes: and I entreated her come forth,
    And bear this work of heaven with patience.
    But then a noise did scare me from the tomb,
    And she, too desperate, would not go with me,
    But as it seems, did violence on herself."

24. One of the plays set in Rome closes with the following lines:
    "Though in this city he
    Hath widowed and unchilded many a one,
    Which to this hour bewail the injury,
    Yet he shall have a noble memory."
    To whom do they refer?

25.   "What's this, what's this? Is this her fault or mine?
        The tempter or the tempted, who sins most?"
    The speaker is Angelo in "Measure for Measure". Who
    is he talking about?

26.   "He took me by the wrist, and held me hard;
        Then goes he to the length of all his arm,
        And, with his other hand thus o'er his brow,
        He falls to such perusal of my face
        As 'a would draw it."
    Who is talking about whom?

27. Tom Stoppard wrote a play about which two characters
    from "Hamlet"?

LOVERS

1. Who describes who as "this enchanting queen"? Is it:
   a) Antony of Cleopatra
   b) Oberon of Titania
   c) Romeo of Juliet ?

2. Who says:
   "She speaks.
   O, speak again, bright angel, for thou art
   As glorious to this night, being o'er my head,
   As is a winged messenger of heaven
   Unto the white-upturned wond'ring eyes of
       mortals that fall back to gaze on him," ?

3. Who says of who in "The Tempest":
   "I might call him
   A thing divine; for nothing natural
   I ever saw so noble." ?

4. Name the characters who say the following in "The Two Gentleman of Verona":
   X: "I have lov'd her ever since I saw her, and still
       I see her beautiful."
   Y: "If you love her, you cannot see her."
   X: "Why?"
   Y: "Because Love is blind." ?

5. "The course of true love never did run smooth;" Is this line from:
   a) "Romeo and Juliet"
   b) "Much Ado About Nothing"
   c) "A Midsummer Night's Dream" ?

6. From which play is this taken?:
    Berowne: "Our wooing doth not end like an old play:
        Jack hath not Jill."

7. In "As You Like It" who says:
    "Troilus had his brains dash'd out with a Grecian
    club; yet he did what he could to die before, and
    he is one of the patterns of love." ?

8. Who says this in "Antony And Cleopatra"?:
    "Give me some music - music, moody food
    Of us that trade in love."

9. In which play is this said and to whom?:
    Celia: "It is young Orlando, that tripp'd up the
        wrestler's heels and your heart both in the
        instant."

10. Where is this taken from? Who is speaking and about
    whom?:
    "She lov'd me for the dangers I had pass'd;
    And I lov'd her that she did pity them."

11. Pair up the lovers from "A Midsummer Night's
    Dream": Hermia, Helena, Lysander and Demetrius.

12. Who says this when her lover dies?:
    "Noblest of men, woo't die? Hast thou no care of
        me? Shall I abide
    In this dull world, which in thy absence is
    No better than a sty? O, see, my women,
    (X dies)
    The crown o'th'earth doth melt."

13. Who says to whom?:

> "Sweet, so would I.
> Yet I should kill thee with much cherishing.
> Good night, good night! Parting is such sweet
>   sorrow
> That I shall say good night till it be morrow."

FAMILY TREES

1. What is the name of Cymbeline's daughter?

2. Richard the Third has two brothers. Can you name them both?

3. What is the name of Isabella's brother in "Measure For Measure"?

4. Whose mother is Queen Elinor?

5. In "Twelfth Night" who is Sir Toby Belch's niece?:
   a) Viola
   b) Olivia
   c) Maria

6. Diana is a character in "All's Well That Ends Well". Whose daughter is she?

7. Who is Katherina and Bianca's father in "The Taming of the Shrew":
   a) Lucentio
   b) Gremio
   c) Baptista ?

8. Gloucester has two sons ("King Lear"). True or False?

9. What relation is Pandarus to Cressida ("Troilus and Cressida") ?

10. Polonius has a daughter ("Hamlet"). What is her name?

11. In "Julius Caesar" who is married to Portia?

12. What is Octavia's relationship to these characters in "Antony and Cleopatra"?
    a) Caesar
    b) Antony

13. Hotspur is whose son in "King Richard The Second"?

14. Can you name the King's two uncles in "King Richard The Second"?

15. What are the names of the warring families in "Romeo and Juliet"?

16. The Old Shepherd is the reputed father of Perdita in "The Winter's Tale". True or false?

17. Which play has in its list of characters: "A son that has killed his father" and "A father that has killed his son"? Is it:
    a) "King Henry the Sixth-Part Three"
    b) "King Henry the Eighth"
    c) "King Richard the Second" ?

18. Beatrice is a character in "Much Ado About Nothing". Whose niece is she?

19. Which family does Romeo belong to?

20. In "Romeo and Juliet" who is Lady Capulet's nephew?

21. In which play are there are two sets of male twins?

22. In "Hamlet" what relation is Hamlet to the present King?

OBSCURE ONES

1. In "Titus Andronicus" who is Queen of the Goths?

2. Who in the list of characters in "Julius Caesar" is described as "a sophist of Cnidos"?

3. "What, Patchbreech, I say!"
   Who says this and in which play?

4. In which play do you find these characters: Roman Senators, Tribunes, a Soothsayer, a Dutch Gentleman, a Spanish Gentleman?

5. Cleopatra has four attendants. Can you name them all?

6. Who says this:
   "Go thy ways, Kate.
   That man i'th' world who shall report he has
   A better wife, let him in nought be trusted
   For speaking false in that." ?

7. Which character in which play is "a banished lord, disguised under the name of Morgan." ?

8. In which plays do you find these stage directions
   a) "Exeunt Shepherd and Clown"?
   b) "He holds her by the hand, silent"?
   c) "Exeunt all but X, Y and Z as fast as may be, frighted."?
   d) "Enter X, leading a dog."?

9. Who says this in which play?:
   X: "Set't down, let's look upon't.
   Y: T'is like a coffin sir.
   X. Whate'er it be,
      'Tis wondrous heavy.
      Wrench it open straight."

10. Who says this? Where?:
    "What a wicked beast was I to disfurnish myself
    against such a good time, when I might ha'shown
    myself honourable!"

11. Who says this to who in which play and about whom
    is X talking?:
    X: "She's making her ready, she'll come straight;
       you must be witty now. She does so blush, and
       fetches her wind so short, as if she were fray'd
       with a sprite. I'll fetch her."

12. Who is speaking in this exchange and in which play?:
    X: "What would your Ladyship?
    Y: Is't near dinner time?
    X: I would it were,
       That you might kill your stomach on your meat
       And not on your maid."

13. Where do you find Lord Bigot, Hubert De Burgh and
    Peter of Pomfret?

14. This is a line from the "Merry Wives of Windsor":
    "Vat is de clock, Jack?"
    Who says it and what is Jack's second name?

15. Name these characters from "Love's Labour's Lost":
    a) Armado's page
    b) the three ladies attending on the Princess

16. Who are "kinsmen to Titus" in "Titus Andronicus"?

17. Give the names of these characters from "The Two Gentlemen of Verona":
    a) Valentine's "foolish rival"
    b) Julia's waiting woman
    c) the "agent for Silvia in her escape"

18. In which play do you find these characters:
    Robert Faulconbridge, Philip the Bastard and Blanch of Spain?

19. Who in "King John" says:
    "He hath a trick of Coeur-de-lion's face;
    The accent of his tongue affecteth him.
    Do you not read some tokens of my son
    In the large composition of this man?" ?

20. Which play opens with this stage direction:
    "Enter Poet, Painter, Jeweller, Merchant and Mercer, at several doors." ?

21. Who says this in which History play and who is he talking to?:
    X: "I pray thee, loving wife, and gentle daughter,
    Give even way unto my rough affairs;"

22. Which play closes with these lines:
    "The words of Mercury are harsh after the songs of Apollo. You that way; we this way;" ?

ANSWERS: NAME THE PLAY

1. "King John", "King Richard The Second", "The First Part Of King Henry The Fourth", "The Second Part Of King Henry The Fourth", "King Henry The Fifth", "The First Part Of King Henry The Sixth", "The Second Part Of King Henry The Sixth", The Third Part Of King Henry The Sixth", "King Richard The Third", "King Henry The Eighth", "Hamlet, Prince of Denmark", "Pericles, Prince of Tyre".

2. "Love's Labour's Lost".

3. "Hamlet".

4. "Othello, The Moor of Venice", "Hamlet, Prince of Denmark", "Twelfth Night; Or What You Will", "Pericles, Prince of Tyre".

5. "The Two Gentlemen Of Verona", "The Merry Wives Of Windsor", "The Merchant Of Venice", "Timon Of Athens", "Hamlet, Prince Of Denmark", "Othello, The Moor Of Venice", "Pericles, Prince Of Tyre".

6. a) "King Henry The Eighth".

7. c) "Much Ado About Nothing".

8. "The Comedy of Errors", "The Two Gentlemen of Verona", "The Taming of the Shrew".

9. "A Midsummer Night's Dream".

10. "King Henry The Fourth - Part Two" and "King Henry The Eighth". "All's Well That Ends Well," "As You Like It" and "The Tempest".

ANSWERS: NAME THE PLAY

11. "Titus Andronicus", "Romeo And Juliet", "Julius Caesar", "Hamlet", "Othello", "Timon Of Athens", "King Lear", "Macbeth", "Antony And Cleopatra", "Coriolanus".

12. "The Comedy Of Errors" and "Measure For Measure".

13. "All's Well That Ends Well".

14. "The Tempest".

15. "The Comedy Of Errors", "The Taming Of The Shrew", "The Two Gentlemen Of Verona", "Love's Labour's Lost", "A Midsummer Night's Dream", "The Merchant Of Venice", "The Merry Wives Of Windsor", "Much Ado About Nothing", "As You Like It", "Twelfth Night", "Troilus And Cressida", "Measure For Measure", "All's Well That Ends Well", "Pericles", "Cymbeline", "The Winter's Tale", "The Tempest".

16. "Measure For Measure" and "All's Well That Ends Well".

17. True.

18. "As You Like It".

19. "King Henry The Fifth", "King Henry The Eighth", "Troilus and Cressida", "Romeo and Juliet".

20. "Macbeth".

21. "King Richard the Third".

22. a) "A Midsummer Night's Dream".

ANSWERS: NAME THE PLAY

23. Seven.

24. "Titus Andronicus".

25. a) "Measure For Measure". b) "The Merry Wives Of Windsor". c) "The Two Gentlemen Of Verona".

26. a) "King Henry The Eighth".

27. a) "The Merchant Of Venice". b) "As You Like It". c) "A Midsummer Night's Dream".

28. "The Tempest".

29. c) "The Taming Of The Shrew".

30. c) "King Henry The Fourth - Part Two".

31. "The First Part of King Henry The Fourth" and "The Second Part of King Henry The Fourth".

ANSWERS: DEATHS AND GORY BITS

1. c) Portia.

2. Romeo poisons himself, Juliet stabs herself.

3. Othello smothers Desdemona.

4. Charmian and Cleopatra ("Antony and Cleopatra").

5. Lady Macbeth (Act 5, Scene 8, l. 70).

ANSWERS: DEATHS AND GORY BITS

6. Antigonus in "The Winter's Tale".

7. a) the Conspirators. b) they stab him. c) Aufidius.

8. c) "King Lear" (Act 5, Scene 3, l. 240).

9. Cleopatra.

10. "Titus Andronicus".

11. b) Gloucester.

12. a) "Titus Andronicus". b) "King Lear".

13. Hamlet (Act 5, Scene 2, l. 344).

14. Macduff with Macbeth's.

15. Lavinia ("Titus Andronicus").

16. Emilia.

17. True.

18. Titus Andronicus.

19. b) Brutus ("Julius Caesar", Act 5, Scene 5, l. 47).

20. Lady Macbeth (Act 2, Scene 2, l. 48).

21. Ophelia.

22. He is stabbed by the conspirators.

23. "Measure for Measure".

ANSWERS: DEATHS AND GORY BITS

24. Titus Andronicus.

25. Antony.

26. From a poisoned sword wound.

27. Cinna the Poet.

28. "Richard the Third".

ANSWERS: GHOSTS, GHOULS AND SPIRITS

1. Brutus in "Julius Caesar" (Act 4, Scene 3, l. 273).

2. First Witch, "Macbeth" (Act 4, Scene 1, l. 4).

3. Caliban.

4. Robin Goodfellow.

5. Ariel.

6. Peaseblossom, Cobweb, Moth and Mustardseed.

7. a) "Julius Caesar" (Act. 1, Scene 3, l. 22).

8. The ghost of Prince Edward (Act 5, Scene 3, l. 118).

9. True ("Richard the Third", Act 5, Scene 3, l. 124).

10. At Philippi (Act 4, Scene 3, l. 281).

11. "Macbeth".

12. b) Puck (Act Two, Scene 1, l. 175).

13. "A Midsummer Night's Dream" (Act Two, Scene 2, l. 9).

14. False. "Macbeth".

15. a) "The Tempest".

16. Diana.

17. Second Witch in "Macbeth" (Act 4, Scene 1, l. 43).

18. Puck (Act 5, Scene 1, l. 412).

19. Prospero to Ariel (Act 1, Scene 2. l. 301).

20. The Weird Sisters.

21. False. Caliban (Act 3, Scene 2, l. 130).

22. Titania.

23. "The Tempest".

24. b) "King Henry The Sixth - Part Two".

25. The ghost of Hamlet's father ("Hamlet", Act 1, Scene 5, l. 9).

1. Calphurnia.

2. Portia.

3. Rosalind.

4. Titania.

5. Mistress Ford, Mistress Page, Mistress Anne Page, Mistress Quickly.

6. Cleopatra and Cressida.

7. a) Volumnia.

8. b) "Measure for Measure".

9. a) "The Two Gentlemen of Verona".

10. Hamlet's.

11. Edward, Prince of Wales (son to King Henry VI).

12. Bianca.

13. Miranda is in "The Tempest"; Perdita is in "The Winter's Tale."

14. Goneril, Regan and Cordelia.

15. Isabella.

16. False. Sebastian.

17. "a rich countess".

18. Leonato's.

19. "King Henry The Fourth - Part Two".

20. c) Katherina in "The Taming Of The Shrew".

21. Portia ("The Merchant Of Venice").

22. True.

23. Juliet (Act 1, Scene 3, l. 18).

24. Lady Macbeth (Act 5, Scene 1, l. 4).

25. First and Second Witches in "Macbeth".

26. a) Cressida ("Troilus And Cressida", Act 5, Scene 2, l. 176).

27. Katherine, "The Taming of the Shrew", (Act 3, Scene 2, ll 216-7)

28. Cordelia ("King Lear", Act 1, Scene 1, l. 90).

29. Lady Macbeth (Act 5, Scene 8, l. 69).

30. Goneril ("King Lear", Act 5, Scene 1, l. 18).

31. Rosalind in "As You Like It".

32. False. Queen Margaret (Act 1, Scene 3, l. 217).

33. c) Imogen ("Cymbeline", Act 3, Scene 6, l. 1).

ANSWERS: FEMALE CHARACTERS

34. Regan of Goneril, "King Lear" (Act 4, Scene 5, l. 23).

ANSWERS: WHO SAID WHAT

1. Anthony in "Julius Caesar" (Act 3, Scene 2, l. 74).

2. a) Othello (Act 5, Scene 2, l. 342).

3. Richard The Third (Act 5, Scene 4, l. 7).

4. Othello (Act 5, Scene 2, l. 346).

5. True (Act 3, Scene 2, l. 144).

6. King Lear (Act 5, Scene 3, l. 257).

7. Hamlet (Act 5, Scene 1, l. 95).

8. b) Coriolanus (Act 5, Scene 3, l. 183).

9. True.

10. Orsino, Duke of Illyria ("Twelfth Night").

11. Shylock (Act 3, Scene 1, l. 58).

12. A Porter in "Macbeth" (Act 2, Scene 3, l. 1).

13. True (Act 3, Scene 1, l. 60).

14. Brutus (Act 4, Scene 3, l. 216).

15. Juliet (Act 2, Scene 2, l. 43).

ANSWERS: WHO SAID WHAT

16. Hamlet (Act 3, Scene 4, l. 28).

17. Portia ("The Merchant Of Venice", Act 4, Scene 1, l. 302).

18. c) Oberon (Act 2, Scene 1, l. 249).

19. Prospero (Act 5, Scene1, l. 50)

20. Phrynia in "Timon Of Athens" (Act 4, Scene 3, l. 63).

21. Casca in "Julius Caesar", (Act 1, Scene 3, l. 20).

22. Polonius ("Hamlet" Act 1, Scene 3, l. 75).

23. c) Iago (Act 2, Scene 3, l. 261).

24. Lady Macbeth (Act 1, Scene 7, l. 60)

25. Hamlet (Act 5, Scene 1, l. 179).

ANSWERS: SET THE SCENE

1. Verona and Mantua.

2. a) "Love's Labour's Lost".

3. "A Midsummer Night's Dream".

4. b) "The Taming Of The Shrew".

5. Rome and the Neighbourhood.

ANSWERS: SET THE SCENE

6. Milan.

7. True.

8. "Othello" and "The Merchant Of Venice".

9. a) Pericles.

10. Scotland and England.

11. "The Tempest".

12. "Julius Caesar", "Titus Andronicus", "Coriolanus".

13. False. "The Winter's Tale".

14. "All's Well That Ends Well".

15. "Measure For Measure".

16. "As You Like It".

17. "Antony And Cleopatra".

18. "A Midsummer Night's Dream" and "Timon Of Athens".

ANSWERS: JOKERS, JESTERS AND CLOWNS

1. "The Tempest".

2. Grave-diggers.

3. a) "The Winter's Tale".

4. Sir John Falstaff, Edward Poins, Bardolph, Pistol, Peto.

5. a) Stephano in "The Tempest". b) Speed and Launce in "The Two Gentlemen Of Verona". c) Touchstone in "As You Like It."

6. Malvolio (Act 5, Scene 1, l. 321).

7. "Twelfth Night".

8. "The Merchant Of Venice".

9. True.

10. The Fool in "King Lear" (Act 3, Scene 2, l. 10).

11. a) "Measure For Measure".

12. Touchstone.

13. Feste, "Twelfth Night".

14. c) "Measure For Measure".

ANSWERS: FINISH THE SPEECH

1. "To be, or not to be - that is the question;/Whether 'tis nobler in the mind to suffer/The slings and arrows of outrageous fortune,/Or to take arms against a sea of troubles,/And by opposing end them? To die, to sleep -/No more; and by a sleep to say we end/The heart-ache and the thousand natural shocks/That flesh is heir to. 'Tis a consummation/Devoutly to be wish'd. To die, to sleep;/To sleep, perchance to dream. Ay, there's the rub;/For in that sleep of death what dreams may come,/When we have shuffled off this mortal coil,/Must give us pause." ("Hamlet", Act 3, Scene 1, l. 56-68).

2. "The quality of mercy is not strain'd;/It droppeth as the gentle rain from heaven/Upon the place beneath. It is twice blest:/It blesseth him that gives and him that takes". ("The Merchant of Venice", Act 4, Scene 1, l. 178-181).

3. "Now is the winter of our discontent/Made glorious summer by this sun of York;/And all the clouds that lour'd upon our house/In the deep bosom of the ocean buried./Now are our brows bound with victorious wreaths;/Our bruised arms hung up for monuments;/Our stern alarums chang'd to merry meetings,/Our dreadful marches to delightful measures." ("King Richard the Third", Act 1, Scene 1, l. 1-7).

4. "All the world's a stage,/And all the men and women merely players./They have their exits and their entrances,/And one man in his time plays many parts,/His acts being seven ages." ("As You Like It, Act 2, Scene 7, l. 139)

5. "But this rough magic/I here abjure; and, when I have requir'd/Some heavenly music - which even now I do - /To work mine end upon their senses that/This airy charm is for, I'll break my staff,/Bury it certain fathoms in the earth,/And deeper than did ever plummet sound/I'll drown my book". ("The Tempest", Act 5, Scene 1, l. 50-57).

6. "Is this a dagger which I see before me,/The handle toward my hand? Come, let me clutch thee./I have thee not, and yet I see thee still./Art thou not, fatal vision, sensible/To feeling as to sight? or art thou but/ A dagger of the mind, a false creation,/Proceeding from the heat-oppressed brain?" ("Macbeth", Act 2, Scene 1, l. 33-39).

7. "Out, damned spot! out, I say! One, two; why then 'tis time to do't. Hell is murky. Fie, my lord, fie! a soldier, and afeard? What need we fear who knows it, when none can call our pow'r to account? Yet who would have thought the old man to have had so much blood in him?" ("Macbeth", Act 5, Scene 1, l. 33).

8. "But soft ! What light through yonder window breaks?/ It is the east, and Juliet is the sun./Arise, fair sun, and kill the envious moon, /Who is already sick and pale with grief/That thou her maid art far more fair than she." ("Romeo and Juliet", Act 2, Scene 2, l. 2-6).

9. "Blow, winds, and crack your cheeks; rage, blow. /You cataracts and hurricanoes, spout/Till you have drench'd our steeples, drown'd the cocks. /You sulph'rous and thought-executing fires, /Vaunt-couriers of oak-cleaving thunderbolts, /Singe my white head. And thou, all-shaking thunder,/Strike flat the

thick rotundity o'th'world;/Crack nature's moulds, all germens spill at once, /That makes ingrateful man." ("King Lear", Act 3, Scene 2, l. 1-9).

10. "O Romeo, Romeo! wherefore art thou Romeo?/Deny thy father and refuse thy name; /Or, if thou wilt not, be but sworn my love,/And I'll no longer be a Capulet." ("Romeo and Juliet", Act 2, Scene 2, l. 33-36).

11. "Friends, Romans, countrymen, lend me your ears; /I come to bury Caesar, not to praise him. /The evil that men do lives after them; /The good is oft interred with their bones; /So let it be with Caesar. The noble Brutus/ Hath told you Caesar was ambitious. /If it were so, it was a grievous fault; /And grievously hath Caesar answer'd it. /Here, under leave of Brutus and the rest -/For Brutus is an honourable man; /So are they all, all honourable men -/Come I to speak in Caesar's funeral." ("Julius Caesar", Act 3, Scene 2, l. 74).

ANSWERS: NAME THE CHARACTER

1. Coriolanus, Titus Andronicus, Timon Of Athens, Julius Caesar, Othello, Pericles, Macbeth, Hamlet, King Lear, Cymbeline.

2. Friar Lawrence.

3. Marcus Brutus, Cassius, Casca, Trebonius, Ligarius, Decius Brutus, Metellus Cimber, Cinna.

ANSWERS: NAME THE CHARACTER

4. a) Orsino, Sebastian, Antonio, Valentine, Curio, Sir Toby Belch, Sir Andrew Aguecheek, Malvolio, Fabian, Feste. Olivia, Viola, Maria.
   b) Christopher Sly, Baptista Minola, Vincentio, Lucentio, Petruchio, Gremio, Hortensio, Tranio, Biondello, Grumio, Curtis. Katherina, Bianca.

5. a) Benedick.

6. Rosalind and "As You Like It"; the Nurse and "Romeo And Juliet"; Desdemona and "Othello".

7. True.

8. "Richard The Second" and "The First Part Of King Henry The Fourth".

9. Goneril, Regan, Cordelia ("King Lear"). Portia, Nerissa, Jessica ("The Merchant of Venice").

10. Cymbeline and Coriolanus.

11. False. They are characters from "Twelfth Night".

12. Ulysses, Nestor, Diomedes, Patroclus.

13. Quince, a carpenter; Snug, a joiner; Bottom, a weaver; Flute, a bellows-maker; Snout, a tinker; Starveling, a tailor.

14. a) Sir Nathaniel, a curate; Holofernes, a schoolmaster; Dull, a constable.

ANSWERS: NAME THE CHARACTER

15. Audrey, "As You Like It"; Jaquenetta, "Love's Labour's Lost".

16. Falstaff ("King Henry The Fourth - Part Two", Act 4, Scene 3, l. 118).

17. a). Othello ("Othello", Act 5, Scene 2, l. 298).

18. Hamlet. (Act 1, Scene 2, l. 70).

19. Richard The Third ("Richard The Third", Act 1, Scene 3, l. 243 and 246).

20. Julius Caesar ("Julius Caesar, Act 1, Scene 2, l. 135).

21. Iago and Othello in "Othello".

22. False. Cassius ("Julius Caesar", Act 1, Scene 2, l. 195).

23. Friar Lawrence about Juliet ("Romeo And Juliet", Act 5, Scene 3, l. 259).

24. Coriolanus.

25. Isabella ("Measure For Measure", Act 2, Scene 2, l. 162).

26. c) Ophelia of Hamlet (Act 2, Scene 1, l. 87).

27. Rosencrantz and Guildenstern.

ANSWERS: LOVERS

1. a) Antony describing Cleopatra ("Antony And Cleopatra", Act 1, Scene 2, l. 125).

2. Romeo (Act 2, Scene 2, l. 25).

3. Miranda of Ferdinand ("The Tempest", Act 1, Scene 2, l. 418).

4. Valentine and Speed ("The Two Gentlemen Of Verona", Act 2, Scene 1, l. 60).

5. c) "A Midsummer Night's Dream", (Act 1, Scene 1, l. 134).

6. "Love's Labour's Lost" (Act 5, Scene 2, l. 862).

7. Rosalind ("As You Like It", Act 4, Scene 1, l. 87).

8. Cleopatra (Act 2, Scene 5, l. 1).

9. "As You Like It", to Rosalind (Act 3, Scene 2, l. 197).

10. "Othello". Othello is talking about Desdemona (Act 1, Scene 3, l. 167).

11. Hermia and Lysander, Helena and Demetrius.

12. Cleopatra when Antony dies ("Antony And Cleopatra", Act 4, Scene 14, l. 59).

13. Juliet to Romeo (Act 2, Scene 2, l. 183).

1. Imogen.

2. King Edward the Fourth and George, Duke of Clarence.

3. Claudio.

4. King John.

5. b) Olivia.

6. The Widow's.

7. c) Baptista.

8. True. Edmund and Edgar.

9. Uncle.

10. Ophelia.

11. Brutus.

12. a) sister. b) wife.

13. The Earl of Northumberland.

14. John of Gaunt and Edmund of Langley.

15. Montague and Capulet.

16. True.

17. a) "King Henry The Sixth - Part Three".

ANSWERS: FAMILY TREES

18. Leonato's.

19. Montague.

20. Tybalt.

21. "The Comedy Of Errors".

22. Nephew.

ANSWERS: OBSCURE ONES

1. Tamora.

2. Artemidorus.

3. First Fisherman, "Pericles", (Act 2, Scene 1, l. 14).

4. "Cymbeline".

5. Alexas, Mardian, Seleucus, Diomedes.

6. The King, "King Henry The Eighth", (Act 2, Scene 4, l. 133).

7. Belarius in "Cymbeline".

8. a) "The Winter's Tale". b) "Coriolanus". c) "The Comedy of Errors". d) "The Two Gentlemen of Verona".

9. Cerimon and Second Gentleman, "Pericles" (Act 3, Scene 2, l. 53).

ANSWERS: OBSCURE ONES

10. Lucius, "Timon of Athens" (Act 3, Scene 2, l. 43).

11. Pandarus to Troilus about Cressida, "Troilus And Cressida" (Act 3, Scene 2, l. 29).

12. Lucetta and Julia, "The Two Gentlemen Of Verona" (Act1, Scene 2, l. 67).

13. "King John".

14. Caius. Rugby (Act 2, Scene 3, l. 3).

15. a) Moth; b) Rosaline, Maria and Katharine.

16. Sempronius, Caius and Valentine.

17. a) Thurio; b) Lucetta; c) Eglamour.

18. "King John".

19. Queen Elinor (Act 1, Scene 1, l. 85).

20. "Timon of Athens".

21. Northumberland, "King Henry The Fourth - Part Two", speaking to Lady Northumberland and Lady Percy (Act 2, Scene 3, l. 1).

22. "Love's Labour's Lost".